A Kiss

Written by Anne Marie Ryan
Illustrated by Rachael O'Neill

WISE WALRUS

What is synthetic phonics?

Synthetic phonics teaches children to recognise the sounds of letters and to blend 'synthesise' them together to make whole words.

Understanding sound/letter relationships gives children the confidence and ability to read unfamiliar words, without having to rely on memory or guesswork; this helps them progress towards independent reading.

Did you know? Spoken English uses more than 40 speech sounds. Each sound is called a *phoneme*. Some phonemes relate to a single letter (d-o-g) and others to combinations of letters (sh-ar-p). When a phoneme is written down it is called a *grapheme*. Teaching these sounds, matching them to their written form and sounding out words for reading is the basis of synthetic phonics.

Consultant

I love reading phonics has been created in consultation with language expert Dr Marlynne Grant (Chartered and Registered Educational Psychologist). For more than 25 years, Marlynne has worked as a regional educational psychologist, specialising in literacy development for children of all abilities.

Reading tips

 A Kiss! focuses on the sounds:
qu, **x**, **ff**, **ll**, **ss**, **zz** and **ck**.

Tricky words in *A Kiss!*

Any words in bold do not sound exactly as they look (don't fit the usual sound–letter rules) or are new and have not yet been introduced.

> ### Tricky words in this book:
>
> **<u>the</u>**   **t<u>o</u>**   **<u>who</u>**   **h<u>e</u>**
>
> **y<u>ou</u>**   **m<u>e</u>**   **s<u>ai</u>d**   **<u>I</u>**

Extra ways to have fun with *A Kiss!*

• After the reader has read the story, ask them questions about what they have just read:

> *Who does Nick try to kiss?*
> *Why does Nick get into a huff?*

• Make flashcards of the focus sounds (qu, x, ff, ll, ss, zz and ck). Ask the reader to say the sounds. This will help reinforce letter/sound matches.

> My big brother listens to me read. He says I'm a very good reader. I like to read in his bedroom.

A pronunciation guide

This grid contains the sounds used in
the story and a guide on how to say them.

s	a	t	p
as in sat	as in ant	as in tin	as in pig
i	n	c	e
as ink	as in net	as in cat	as in egg
h	r	m	d
as in hen	as in rat	as in mug	as in dog
g	o	u	l
as in get	as in ox	as in up	as in log
f	b	j	v
as in fan	as in bag	as in jug	as in van
w	z	y	k
as in wet	as in zip	as in yet	as in kit
qu	x	ff	ll
as in quiz	as in box	as in off	as in fill
ss	zz	ck	
as in hiss	as in buzz	as in duck	

Be careful not to add an 'uh' sound to 's', 't', 'p',
'c', 'h', 'r', 'm', 'd', 'g', 'l', 'f' and 'b'. For example,
say 'fff' not 'fuh' and 'sss' not 'suh'.

Nick **the** duck sits on a dock.

Bugs buzz and kiss.

Nick is off **to** get a kiss.

Who will **he** pick?

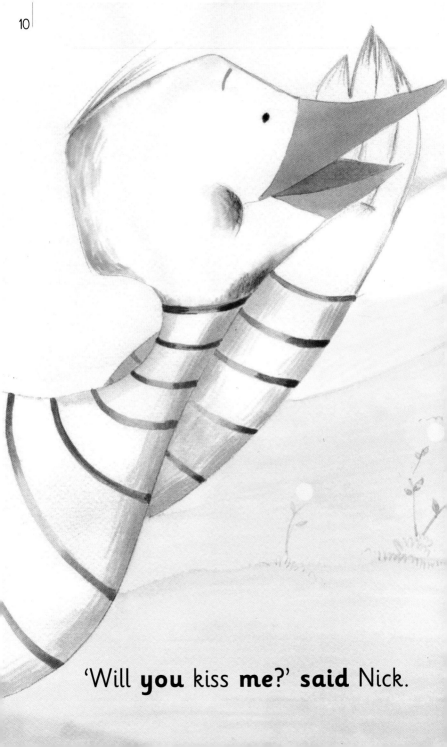

'Will **you** kiss **me**?' **said** Nick.

'Buzz off,' **said** an ox on **the** hill.

'Kiss **me**, quick!' **said** Nick.

'**I** will pass,' **said** a hen on a box.

'Can **I** just get a kiss?' **said** Nick.

'Back off,' **said** a cat on a rock.

'Kiss?' **said** Nick.

'Yuck!' **said** a fox as **he** zips off.

Nick is in a huff!

But Nick is in luck!

Viv is at **the** well.

Peck!
Nick has a kiss on his bill.

'Quack!' **said** Nick.

Other **Level 1** titles to enjoy:

978-1-84898-277-2

978-1-84898-390-8

978-1-84898-396-0

Other titles in the series

Level **2**

978-1-84898-386-1

978-1-84898-387-8

978-1-84898-388-5

Beth and the Bugs
978-1-84898-389-2

Level **3**

978-1-84898-397-7

978-1-84898-398-4

978-1-84898-399-1

978-1-84898-400-4

Copyright © Wise Walrus Ltd 2011
First published in Great Britain in 2011 by Wise Walrus
The Pantiles Chambers, 85 High Street, Tunbridge Wells, Kent TN1 1XP
ISBN: 978-1-84898-391-5
Printed in China 10 9 8 7 6 5 4 3 2 1